cla

LIFE
SAVERS

classroom
LIFE
SAVERS

PETER
CLUTTERBUCK

Level Two

Ashton Scholastic

SYDNEY AUCKLAND NEW YORK TORONTO LONDON

To the memory of Martin Carboon

The purchase of this book entitles the teacher to reproduce the black-line masters for classroom use.

Typeset by Interset Pty Ltd, Beenleigh, Qld
Printed by Star Printery Pty Limited, Erskinville, NSW

10 9 8 7 6 5 4 3 2   7 8 9 / 8 0 1 2 3 / 9

Introduction

How many times during the school day do you wish there was something extra to give the class? Students often finish work early, have free time, need inspiring on rainy days, want a refreshing change to the usual homework tasks or need a 'brain warmer' at certain times of the day. *CLASSROOM LIFESAVERS* rescues you from all those moments.

For students who are coping more than adequately with a particular area of the curriculum there is nothing to be gained in providing more of the same. Such practices create a great deal of boredom and frustration for the learner.

The problem of catering for students who consistently finish their work earlier than the rest of the class has long concerned teachers. The class teacher is so often occupied with assisting the slower learners that little effort can be made in providing worthwhile activities for these children.

CLASSROOM LIFESAVERS has been designed to provide the challenges these children so desperately need. Activities are carefully graded in six major areas.

1　**Word puzzles**
2　**Maths puzzles**
3　**General Knowledge**
4　**Puzzles**
5　**Make and do**
6　**Games to play**

There is no preparation needed by the class teacher as the activities are self-explanatory and apart from a pencil and paper generally no other equipment is needed.

A reproducible Student Record is included and answers are provided at the back of the book.

Word Puzzles, Maths Puzzles and General Knowledge activities have been designed so that they can be photocopied and mounted on cards. The cards can then be kept in a box in an easily accessible area. Early finishers may then go and get a card and continue quietly without disturbing the rest of the class.

There are, however, no hard and fast rules — in fact the activities will lend themselves to a multitude of uses. Substitute teachers will wonder how they ever survived without *LIFESAVERS* — a wealth of fully reproducible activity sheets ready to use with students of any level.

Level Two is designed for use with students in Years 3-5. **Level One** provides individual, fully-reproducible worksheets for Years 1-3 and **Level Three** caters for Years 5-7 in a similar format to Level Two.

However you use them, *CLASSROOM LIFESAVERS* will make every minute in the classroom count. They will spark every student's idle moment.

Student Record

Name:

| Word Puzzles | 1 | 2 | 3 | 4 | 5 | 6 | 7 | 8 | 9 | 10 | 11 | 12 | 13 | 14 | 15 | 16 | 17 | 18 | 19 | 20 |
| | 21 | 22 | 23 | 24 | 25 | 26 | 27 | 28 | 29 | 30 | 31 | 32 | 33 | 34 | 35 | 36 | 37 | 38 | 39 | 40 |

| Maths Puzzles | 1 | 2 | 3 | 4 | 5 | 6 | 7 | 8 | 9 | 10 | 11 | 12 | 13 | 14 | 15 | 16 | 17 | 18 | 19 | 20 |

| General Knowledge | 1 | 2 | 3 | 4 | 5 | 6 | 7 | 8 | 9 | 10 | 11 | 12 | 13 | 14 | 15 | 16 | 17 | 18 | 19 | 20 |

| Puzzles | 1 | 2 | 3 | 4 | 5 | 6 | 7 | 8 | 9 | 10 | 11 | 12 | 13 | 14 | 15 | 16 | 17 | 18 | 19 | 20 |

| Make and Do | 1 | 2 | 3 | 4 | 5 | 6 | 7 | 8 | 9 | 10 |

| Games to Play | 1 | 2 | 3 | 4 | 5 | 6 | 7 | 8 | 9 | 10 |

Word Puzzles

Find the 'sh'

Colour all the things in the picture which have 'sh' in them. Write the words on a sheet of paper.

Word Puzzles

Word wheel

How many different words can you find on this wheel? Move around the wheel in a clockwise direction and write down each word you find. Do not change the order of the letters.

Test

There

Reel

Scrambled soup

By unscrambling the letters in the bowl, can you work out what ingredients have been used to make this soup?

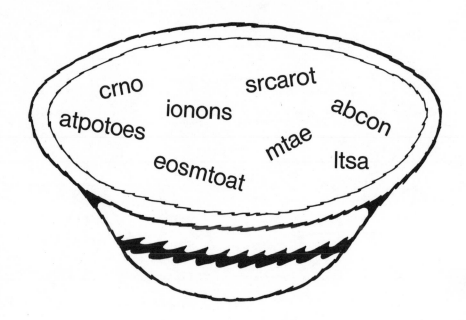

How well do you read?

Read the first passage very carefully. In the second passage find all the changes which have been made. A word may have been left out, added, or changed. Look carefully for punctuation marks, capital letters and spelling.

'All went well with Willie for the first few days of the journey. He loved to sit by the camp fire at night and listen to the tales the drovers told of their lives in the bush. The burning wood on the fire had a sweet smell, and the stars above in the sky looked very big and bright as Willie lay wrapped in his rug, staring up at them before he fell asleep.'

'All went well with willie four the first two days of the journey he loved to sit bye the camp fire at night and listen to the tails the drovers told of their lifes in the scrub. The burning grass on the fire had a sweet smell, and the planets above in the sky looked very shiny and bright as Willy lay wrapt in his blanket, staring up at them before she fell asleep.'

Word Puzzles

Scrambled words

Make two words from the letters in each circle.

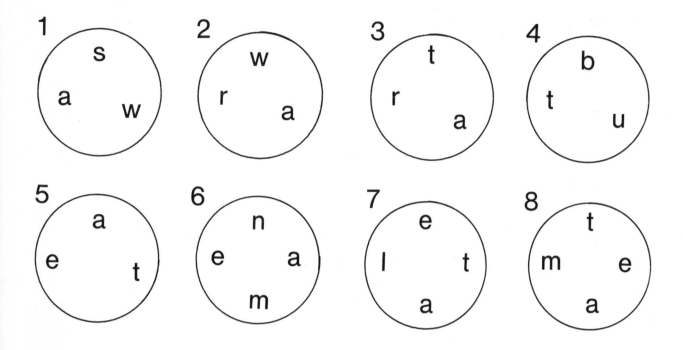

Word Puzzles

Find the word

Trace the line from the picture to the box. Write in the letter that each object begins with. When you have completed the boxes you will have the name of a special event in the year.

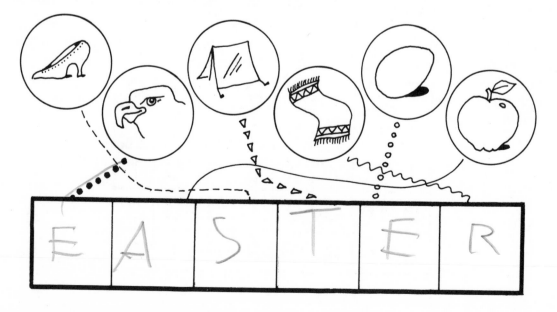

Creature crossword

Identify the animals in the pictures then write each name in the crossword.

Across 1

3

4

6

Down 2 3 5

Word grid

How many foods can you find in this grid? You should be able to find twelve.

p	b	r	e	a	d	x	s
i	a	i	g	p	c	x	t
c	c	c	g	p	h	f	o
k	o	e	s	l	e	l	r
l	n	x	x	e	e	o	r
e	m	e	a	t	s	u	a
s	j	a	m	a	e	r	c

Anagrams

Anagrams are words made by rearranging all the letters of another word.
Rearrange the letters of these words to make another word.

1   Rearrange net and get a number.
2   Rearrange war and get something that is not cooked.
3   Rearrange grin and get something you wear on a finger.
4   Rearrange hips and get a large boat.
5   Rearrange stew and get a direction.
6   Rearrange stop and get what you use in a fence.
7   Rearrange low and get a bird.
8   Rearrange rats and get something that twinkles.
9   Rearrange fringe and get a part of the hand.
10 Rearrange lump and get a fruit.

Word pieces

Join the pairs of letters in each row to make two words.

eg   ga sh me ip = game ship

1   op st lk mi = _____
2   ll ba co at = _____
3   ni ne nd wi = _____
4   sh ck du ut = _____
5   fr fa om rm = _____
6   me bi at rd = _____
7   or so do ft = _____
8   im sw ba by = _____

Keep a secret

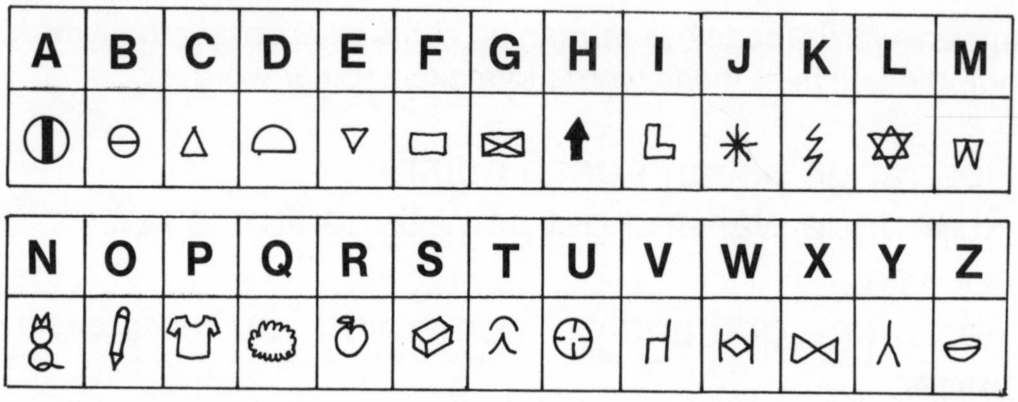

A	B	C	D	E	F	G	H	I	J	K	L	M
◑	⊖	△	⌓	▽	▭	⊠	↑	⌐	✳	⚡	✡	�闪

N	O	P	Q	R	S	T	U	V	W	X	Y	Z
🐱	✎	👕	🌰	🍎	▱	⌃	⊕	⊓	⋈	▷◁	λ	⌣

By reading the code above, can you work out what the following message is?

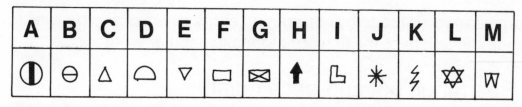

WIPE YOUR FEET BEFORE

ENTERING OUR HOME

Words from words

How many smaller words can you make using the letters in

ARITHMETIC

What's the word?

Here are the last two letters of ten four-letter words. What is each word?

1 __ __ te 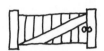   6 __ __ on

2 __ __ by   7 __ __ of

3 __ __ st   8 __ __ ld

4 __ __ lk   9 __ __ ne

5 __ __ in   10 __ __ ke

Join-up

Can you match the names of the drawings to make compound words? Write down the new words.

Word Puzzles

The same letters

Two words in each row have exactly the same letters. Can you find them?

1.   seat meat east star feast
2.   snore shore horse force hoarse
3.   mate male lane steel tame
4.   frigid finish spider fringe finger
5.   listen glisten single legging silent
6.   charm chart march mark made
7.   cedar dear cared bared dread
8.   tackle battle tablet castle crackle
9.   bleat table bloat least treble
10. minute statue tutor astute tatters

Word Puzzles

Hard to easy

Can you change HARD to EASY in five moves? First of all change one letter of HARD and write the new word in the second line. Now change a letter of this new word and write it in the next line, and so on. Clues for each word have been given to help you.

H A R D

__ __ __ __   There are fifty-two in a pack.

__ __ __ __   A horse pulls one.

__ __ __ __   A fisherman does this.

__ __ __ __   A direction.

E A S Y

What's the opposite?

Place a word in the space at the end of each line that is opposite in meaning to the underlined word. There are rhymes to help you.

1 A rock is <u>heavy</u> but a feather is _____.

2 We play during the <u>day</u> but sleep at _____.

3 My bicycle is <u>new</u> but Dad's is _____.

4 The sun is <u>hot</u> but ice is _____.

5 Silk is <u>smooth</u> but gravel is _____.

6 Some meat is <u>tender</u> but some is _____.

7 A minute is <u>short</u> but an hour is _____.

8 A tiny-tot is <u>weak</u> but a giant is _____.

9 A leopard is <u>wild</u> but a puppy is _____.

10 These words are all <u>different</u>; none are the _____.

Hidden words

How many words can you find hidden in these lines without altering the order of the letters?

1 Largest range therein is often desired.

2 Together early allows advances towards artistic ideals.

Word-make

How many words can you make by using the letters in the grid? All the words must contain the letter E.

E	b	a
	t	s
l	m	n
r	z	w
h	c	p

Missing letters

All of these words have a set of double letters missing. Can you work out the letters and complete each word? The pictures will help you.

1   ball __ __ n

2   ch __ __ se

3   ru __ __ er

4   ra __ __ it

5   bo __ __ le

6   je __ __ y

7   fu __ __ el

8   po __ __ y

9   ca __ __ ot

10   dre __ __

Letter change

Change one letter in each word to make a new word to fit the picture.

1   hope

2   band

3   sight

4   cart

5   wafer

6   show

7   monkey

8   marrow

9   boast

10   grant

'Ssh!' Silent letters

All these things have a silent letter in their names. Write the name and circle the silent letter.

Animal pieces

When the lion roared all the creatures scattered into the jungle. However their names got a little mixed up. Can you match the word parts to make the names of the creatures?

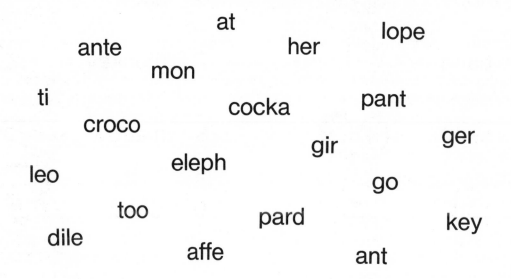

Wise old saying

Hidden in the circle of letters is a wise old saying. To find out the saying, start at the 'T'. Write down every second letter as you go around the circle. Go around the circle twice.

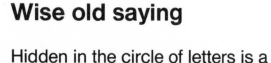

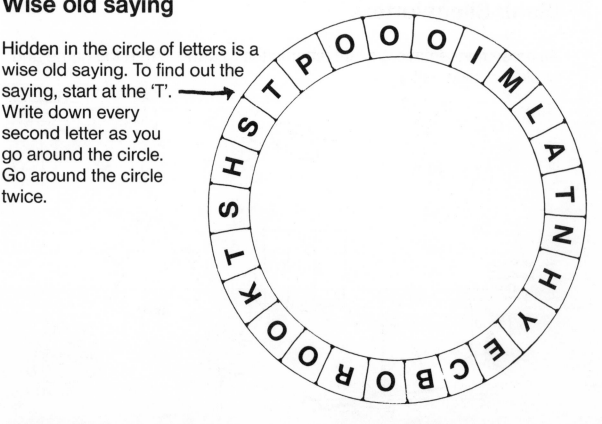

How well do you read?

Read the first passage very carefully. Changes have been made in the second passage. Can you find them all? Some words and punctuation have been left out, some words have been spelt wrongly. You should be able to find at least twenty changes.

'Once there was a good old man who lived up on a high plain, far away in Japan. All around his little house the land was flat and the ground was rich, and there were the rice fields of all the people who lived in the village at the mountain's foot. Every morning and every evening the old man and his little grandson, who lived with him, used to look far down on the people at work in the village, and watch the blue sea which lay all around the land so close that there was no room for fields below but only for houses.'

'Once their was an old man who lived on a low plane, far away in China. All around his big house the land was hilly and the ground was rich and their were the rice fields of all the people who lived in the city at the mountains foot. Every afternoon and every evening the young man and his little grand-daughter, who lived with him, used to look far down on the people at work in the villages and watch the green see witch lay all around the land so close that there were no room for fields below but only for homes.'

Scrambled words

Make two words from the letters in each circle.

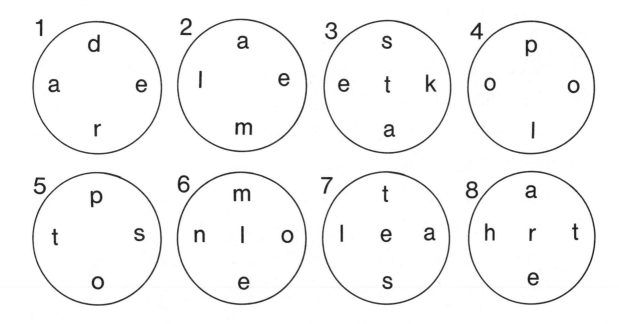

1. d a e r
2. a l e m
3. s e t k a
4. p o o l
5. p t s o
6. m n l o e
7. t l e a s
8. a h r t e

Word grid

This word grid is quite tricky. What you must do is find a word in the grid that sounds the same as the word in the box but has a different spelling and meaning.

s	p	e	a	r	s	h	d	h
c	e	l	l	i	t	a	e	e
e	a	w	o	n	e	r	e	a
n	c	s	u	n	a	e	r	r
t	e	x	d	b	l	e	w	x

pair	in
piece	hair
allowed	here
sell	dear
sent	blue
steel	one
son	

Anagrams

These are words made by rearranging the letters of another word. Rearrange all the letters in the first word to make a word that fits the definition.

1 Rearrange charm and get what soldiers do.
2 Rearrange cheap and get a fruit.
3 Rearrange bleat and get a piece of furniture.
4 Rearrange blow and get a dish.
5 Rearrange paws and get an insect.
6 Rearrange thorn and get a direction.
7 Rearrange lamp and get part of the hand.
8 Rearrange tinsel and get quiet.

Word pieces

Join a word piece in the circle to a word piece in the box to make the names of ten sports or pastimes.

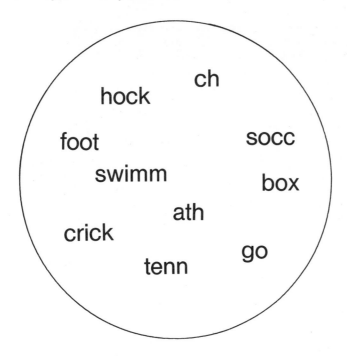

Word Puzzles

ACTIVITY **30**

Keep a secret

Study the code below and then find out what each word is.

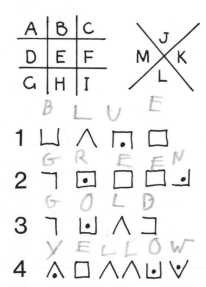

1 BLUE

2 GREEN

3 GOLD

4 YELLOW

5 BLACK

6 BROWN

7 PURPLE

8 WHITE

Words from words

How many words can you make by rearranging the letters of this Victorian town?

SHEPPARTON

————— ————— ————— —————

————— ————— ————— —————

————— ————— ————— —————

————— ————— ————— —————

What's the word?

Here are the last three letters of 10 six-letter words. What is each word?

1 _ _ _ bit

2 _ _ _ ket

3 _ _ _ ten

4 _ _ _ mer

5 _ _ _ key

6 _ _ _ dle

7 _ _ _ ton

8 _ _ _ ana

9 _ _ _ ese

10 _ _ _ rch

Word Puzzles

Where do they belong?

Place each of the words under the headings below. You may need a dictionary to help you.

hamburger cannelloni shirt casserole aquamarine parsnip ruby blouse apartment leotard tie purple stable khaki web igloo

FOOD	CLOTHING	COLOURS	HOMES
_____	_____	_____	_____
_____	_____	_____	_____
_____	_____	_____	_____
_____	_____	_____	_____

Word Puzzles

Back-to-front words

The first part of each of these words has been written last. Can you write each word correctly?

1   oolsch
2   leapp
3   keydon
4   agondr
5   latechoco

6   dowwin
7   phantele
8   etplan
9   enkitch
10   boardcup

Slow to fast

Can you change SLOW to FAST in seven steps? First of all change
one letter of SLOW to make a new word, and write it in the second
line. Now change one letter in this new word to make another word,
and so on. Clues have been given to help you.

S L O W

__ __ __ __   You__ __ __ __ out the candles on the cake.

__ __ __ __   A drop of ink makes this.

__ __ __ __   Like a shoe only larger.

__ __ __ __   We row one across the river.

__ __ __ __   We wear it in cold weather

__ __ __ __   The price of something.

__ __ __ __   A fisherman does this.

F A S T

Jumbled animals

If you rearrange all the letters left out of each alphabet you should be
able to make the name of an animal.

1   _ b c d _ f g _ i j k l m n o p q _ s t u v w x y z

2   a b c d _ f _ h _ j k l m n o p q _ s _ u v w x y z

3   _ _ c d _ f g h i j k l m n o p q _ s t u v w x y z

4   a b c d e f g h _ j k _ m _ _ _ p q r s t u v w x y z

5   a b c d _ f g h i j k l _ n _ p q r _ t _ v w x y z

6   a b c d _ f g _ i j k l m n _ p q _ _ t u v w x y z

7   _ _ c d _ f g h i j k l m n o p q _ s t u v w x y _

8   _ b c d _ f g _ i j k l m _ o _ q _ s _ u v w x y z

9   _ b c d e f _ h i j k l m n _ p q r s _ u v w x y z

Find the fruits and vegetables

In each word pair below there is a hidden fruit or vegetable. Can you find them?

1   astra dishes
2   dump early
3   scar rotten
4   teacher rye
5   hope aches

6   flap luminous
7   maybe answers
8   human goes
9   cartoon ionosphere
10   teapot atoll

Word-make

How many words can you make? Start at any letter and follow the lines to the other letters in any direction, eg mat.

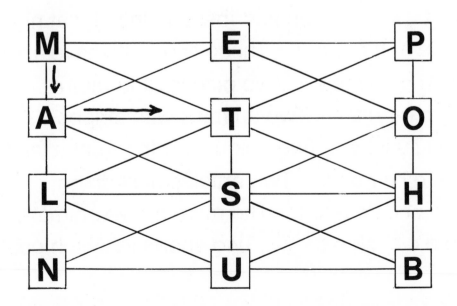

Word Puzzles

What's the saying?

Drop one letter and unscramble the left-over letters to make a word. If you do it correctly you will have a well-known saying when you read downwards.

1 whine_____
2 heat_____
3 scats_____
4 alway_____
5 then_____
6 chime_____
7 swill_____
8 palmy_____

Word Puzzles

Two in one

Each group of letters contains two words with their letters kept in the right order. Can you find the words from the clues given?

1 m s o t o a n r   You find these in the sky at night.
2 o l r e a m n o g n e   These two fruits have a lot of vitamin
3 l t o a u b n l g e e   Two pieces of furniture.
4 z t e i b g r e a r   Two animals with stripes.
5 w b h l i u t e e   Two colours on the Australian flag.
6 b s l h o i u r s t e   Two articles of clothing.
7 m b u a z t c t o o n n   The meat of two animals.
8 s h o o c c c k e e r y   Two sports in which goals are score

Maths Puzzles

Planet puzzler

Pluto Neptune Uranus Saturn Jupiter Mars Earth Venus Mercury

Professor Planet Jumper will soon be blasting off for one of the planets.

Can you discover the planet he is going to visit from these clues? *U ranus*

- It is smaller than Saturn but larger than Mars.
- It is not as close to the Sun as Venus but not as far from the Sun as Neptune.
- It is closer to Pluto than to Mars.

Maths Puzzles

Find the squares

How many different squares (including overlapping ones) can you find in this picture?

Maths Puzzles

Maths cross

By working out the problems, fill in the squares in this puzzle.

Across

1   90 + 10 + 20 + 24 =

3   3 x 7 =

5   4 x 4 =

7   10 x 10 x 4 =

Down

1   11 x 11 =

2   10 + 20 + 10 + 2 =

3   12 x 10 =

6   8 x 8 =

Maths Puzzles

Number codes

By completing correctly the mathematical sentences below, can you work out what each animal is?

Code

A	B	C	E	I	L	M	N	O	R
15	16	25	20	30	40	10	24	18	9

eg 20 + 5 = C, 13 + 2 = A, 3 x 4 = T – CAT

1   10 + 10 + 5 = , 3 x 5 = , 6 + 4 = , 30 – 10 = ,
20 + 20 =   CAMEL

2   12 + 4 = , 12 + 8 = 20 - 5 = , 4 + 5 =   BEAR

3   50 – 10 = , 1/2 x 60 = , 20 – 2 = , 2 x 12 =   LION

(handwritten in margin) 1) 25+15+ 2) 16+

Maths Puzzles

Magic triangle

Arrange the numbers 1, 2, 3, 4, 5 and 6 in the spaces of this triangle so that the numbers on each side of the triangle add up to nine.

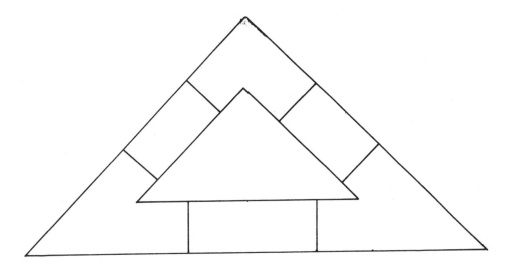

Maths Puzzles

Magic squares

Complete each Magic Square by filling in the missing numbers. The numbers across, down and diagonally, when added, should all equal nine.

4		5
	2	

	6	2
4		

6		
	4	4

Maths puzzles

1   Which of these numbers is the odd one out?
    18, 24, 16, 27, 12

2   One of these watch faces is divided so that the numbers in each
    half add up to the same number. Can you find the correct one?

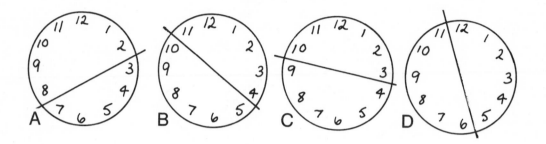

3   How many 250 g chocolate bars are there in a dozen?

Circle patterns

Use a compass to draw a large circle. Mark 12 points around the
circumference like a clock face.

Join each point to every other point,
ie join 1 to 2, 3, 4, 5, 6, 7, 8, 9,
10, 11 and 12. Then join 2 to 3,
4, 5, 6, 7, 8, 9, 10, 11 and 12.
Make sure the lines you rule
are straight. You can use a
different colour for each
point if you wish.

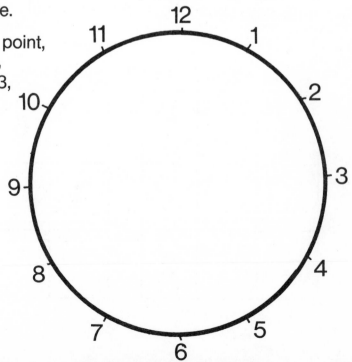

Four square

Four rectangular pieces of card are arranged as below. By moving only one of these cards, make a square.

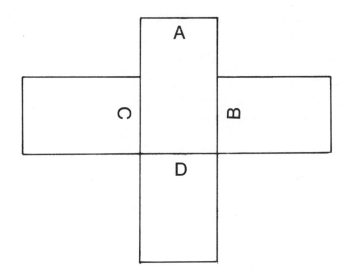

Crack the code

By completing the mathematical sentences below, can you work out what each vehicle is?

A B L N O R S U V Y
24 15 20 22 18 36 54 99 12 84

1   5 x 3 = , 11 x 3 x 3 = , 6 x 9 =
2   7 + 5 = , 8 x 3 = , 18 + 4 =
3   24 − 4 =, 6 x 3 = , 3 x 12 = , 18 x 2 = , 75 + 9 =

Where do they fit?

	Column 1	Column 2
Row 1		
Row 2		

1   To complete this puzzle use only the numbers 1, 2, 3, 4. Use each number only once.

2   The odd numbers are in different columns and the even numbers are not in the same row.

3   The total of row 1 is less than the total of row 2.

4   The 1 is not in row 1 column 1.

Funny fifteens

Place one of the numbers 1, 2, 3, 4, 5, 6, 7, 8 or 9 in each circle so that each set of numbers in a straight line adds up to 15.
(Two numbers have been given to help you.)

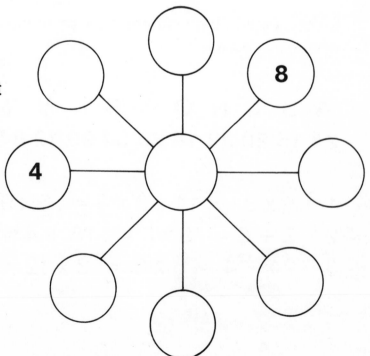

Maths Puzzles

Tricky twelves

Write each of the numbers 1, 2, 3, 4, 5, 6 or 7 in the seven spaces in the beetle. Do this so that every line of three numbers adds up to 12.

Maths Puzzles

Number cross

Work out the problems and fill the numbers in the squares.

Across

1   $200 + 100 + 20 + 206 =$

4   $2000 + 2000 + 200 + 48 + 200 =$

6   $600 - 2 =$

8   $64 \div 8 =$

9   $8 \times 7 =$

10   $49 \div 7 =$

Down

1   $70 - 16 =$

2   $3 \times 8 =$

3   $8 \times 8 =$

5   $12 \times 7 =$

6   $100 - 45 =$

7   $20 + 20 + 30 + 6 + 20 =$

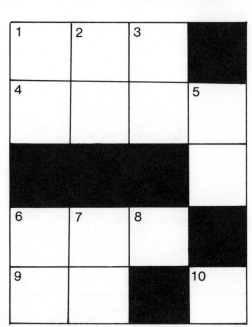

Number codes

By using the number code for each letter, work out what each bird is by completing the number facts.

Code

A	E	H	K	L	N	O	R	W
40	20	24	28	16	12	60	18	30

eg 5 x 4 = , 10 x 10 = , 10 x 5 = emu

1   10 x 6 = , 5 x 6 = , 4 x 4 = *OWL*

2   6 x 5 = , 2 x 9 = , 2 x 10 = , 3 x 4 = *WREN*

3   2 x 12 = , 5 x 8 = , 2 x 15 = , 7 x 4 = *HAWK*

Dot-to-dot

Draw dot-to-dot, counting by fours.
Start at 3.

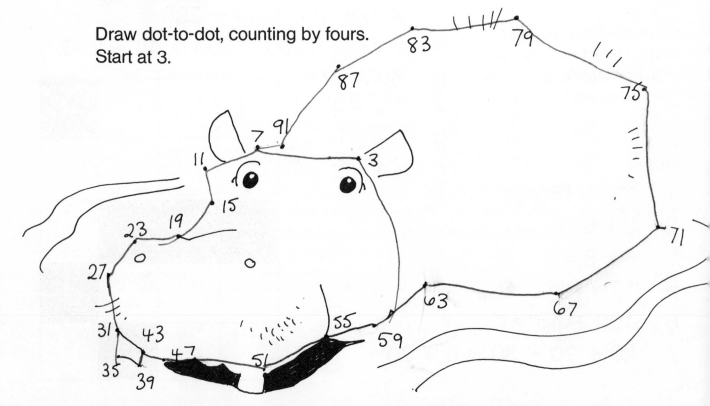

Magic squares

Complete each Magic Square. The total of the numbers across, down and diagonally should equal the number at the top.

9

	2	
0		
4		

12

7		1
		5

18

11	2	
	10	

---

1   John had 18 jelly beans. He ate all but four. How many did he have left to share with Peter and Joan?

2   How many times can you take 3 away from 18?

3   How many months have 28 days?

4   The Parkville Football Club has 36 jumpers for their senior and reserve teams. There are 18 jumpers for each team. The jumpers have numbers on the back only. My friend Jan has been asked to sew the numbers on. How many figure 1s will she need for the 36 jumpers?

5   Which of these numbers is the odd one out?   6 11 18 12 9 21

Maths Puzzles

Colour by numbers

Blue — 16
Red — 10
Orange — 8
White — 20
Purple — 15
Yellow — 5

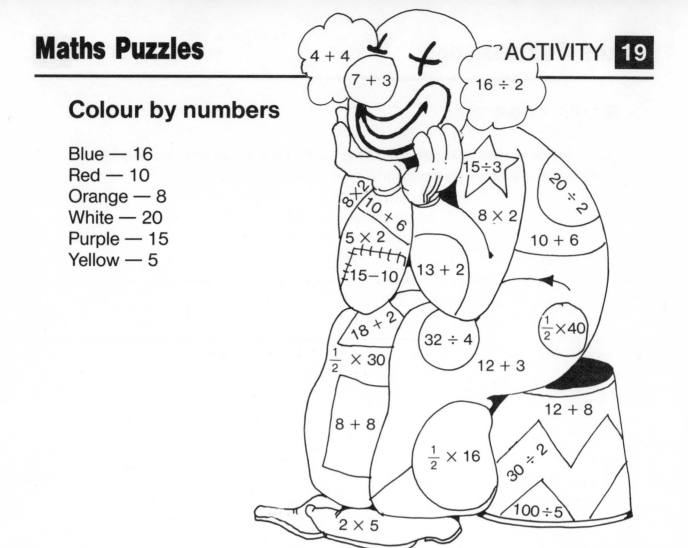

Maths Puzzles

Number maze

Can you find your way through the haunted house? Begin at the front door. You must get to the back door. As you travel along the paths, you must add the numbers in the big circles and subtract the numbers in the squares. You only get to the back door when you have the number 30. You may not travel along the same path twice. If you make a mistake you can start again.

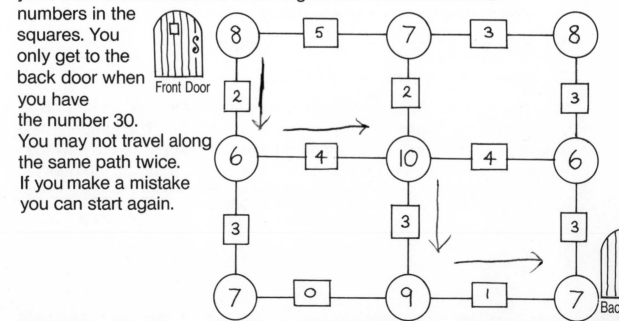

General Knowledge

1. How many zeros do you use when you write twenty thousand?
2. For what do the initials GPO stand?
3. What is the name given to the Olympic sport of spear-throwing?
4. What is a flying fox?
5. In what part of your body would you find your iris?
6. In which story is a wolf disguised as an old lady?
7. Which is the second month of the year having exactly 30 days?
8. What sort of creature is Winnie the Pooh?
9. If you are 'out of sorts', how do you feel?
10. In what city were the 1984 Olympic Games held?

General Knowledge

1. What is chablis?
2. In what part of your body would you find a hammer and an anvil?
3. How many legs does a spider have?
4. In what sport do you hear the terms 'love', 'deuce' and 'fault'?
5. Write these words in alphabetical order:
   gun, rifle, cannon, bomb
6. What is a billabong?
7. Carpet is to floor as __ __ __ __ __ is to window.
8. What season is it in June, July and August, in the Southern Hemisphere?
9. Which word is out of place?
   apricot, radish, nectarine, peach
10. Give a four-letter word that means the opposite of entrance.

General Knowledge

1. For what do the initials PTO stand?
2. Bendigo, Ballarat, Geelong are all cities in which Australian state?
3. Clock is to time as __ __ __ __ __ is to length.
4. What does 'to get into hot water' mean?
5. In what part of the body would you find your Adam's apple?
6. Write the words of which these are the shortened forms:
   Mr, photo, Ave
7. Flock is to sheep as __ __ __ __ __ is to grapes.
8. Who went up the hill to fetch a pail of water?
9. What animal scares away its enemies by giving off a strong smell?
10. In what story would you meet the Cheshire Cat and the Mad Hatter?

General Knowledge

1. What planet starts with the letter V?
2. What type of creatures are dalmatians, terriers and poodles?
3. What are the three colours of a traffic light?
4. If you mix red and blue paint, what colour do you get?
5. With what sport do we associate the Melbourne Cup?
6. What is a surgeon?
7. Up is to down as black is to __ __ __ __ __ .
8. Which word is out of place?
   spider, grasshopper, ant, wasp
9. Rearrange the letters of 'lump' to get a fruit.
10. If a cricketer makes a century, how many runs has he made?

General Knowledge

1   Persian, tabby, and Siamese are all types of what creature?
2   Guitars, pianos and violins are all types of __ __ __ __ __ __ __
    __ __ __ __ __ __ __ __ __ .
3   Name one bird of prey.
4   In what sport can you score a bullseye?
5   What was Miss Muffet frightened by?
6   What colours are found on the Australian flag?
7   What is meant by 'let the cat out of the bag'?
8   What is the name given to the person who looks after you on an aeroplane?
9   What seven months of the year have 31 days?
10   On what date is Anzac Day?

General Knowledge

1   What is a container for paper money called?
2   Which word is out of place?
    netball, soccer, football, chess
3   Bacon is a meat of which animal?
4   Daffodils, carnations and violets are all types of
    __ __ __ __ __ __ __ .
5   What letters are the vowels of the alphabet?
6   What is the name given to the framework of bones in your body?
7   Boat is to pier as train is to __ __ __ __ __ __ __ .
8   What colour is a ruby?
9   Rearrange the letters of 'meat' to get a friend.
10   On what part of your body would you find your scalp?

General Knowledge

1   Name one musical instrument you must blow.
2   Which one of these is a reptile?
    gnat, alligator, wombat, platypus
3   Which of these is out of place?
    maroon, blue, gold, meat
4   What instrument is used to take photographs?
5   What large cat has spots?
6   In what country of the world do people wear wooden shoes
    called clogs?
7   What month of the year begins Autumn?
8   Newcastle, Wollongong and Grafton are all cities in which
    Australian state?
9   What is strange about these words?
    radar, eve, Glenelg
10 How many wheels does a tricycle have?

General Knowledge

1   What is the fruit of an oak tree called?
2   Who couldn't the king's horses and men put together again?
3   In what sport can you play both doubles and singles?
4   Husband is to wife as stallion is to __ __ __ __ .
5   What do we call photographs taken through the body?
6   'Too many cooks spoil the __ __ __ __ __ .'
7   What word means the opposite of give?
8   Which word is out of place?
    panther, lion, beaver, jaguar
9   In which large Australian city would you find both an Opera
    House and a Harbour Bridge?
10 What is the name of the organ that pumps blood around your
    body?

General Knowledge

1 Who was Captain Moonlight?
2 What insect makes honey?
3 In what Australian city would you find the Australian War Memorial?
4 A tadpole is the young of what creature?
5 How many sisters did Cinderella have?
6 Put this list in alphabetical order:
   lion, monkey, ape, giraffe
7 Hand is to writing as __ __ __ is to listening.
8 Which word is out of place?
   carp, herring, cod, eagle
9 What is the home of a dog called?
10 What are you doing if you are 'acting the goat'?

General Knowledge

1 Pig is to sty as horse is to __ __ __ __ __ __ .
2 Which animal has a very long neck?
3 Perth is to Western Australia as Melbourne is to

   __ __ __ __ __ __ __ .
4 A word that means the opposite of stupid is __ __ __ __ __ .
5 Rearrange all the letters of 'plate' to get part of a flower.
6 What sport uses gloves and a ring?
7 Which word is out of place?
   diamond, opal, ring, ruby
8 What is the name of a container for holding flowers?
9 What is the name, beginning with 'c', which is the group name for knives, forks and spoons?
10 In the song 'Waltzing Matilda', what is a jumbuck?

General Knowledge

1   How many legs has a grasshopper?
2   In what sport do you need waves and a board?
3   What is the sixteenth letter of the alphabet?
4   Name three birds that cannot fly.
5   The Murray River divides New South Wales and

    _ _ _ _ _ _ _ .
6   Complete this saying. 'It's no use crying over spilt _ _ _ _ .
7   What country has the longest wall in the world?
8   Flock is to sheep as _ _ _ _ is to cattle.
9   What type of creatures are mackerel and sardines?
10 In what part of your body would you find wisdoms and molars?

General Knowledge

1   Which of these is a citrus fruit?
    apple, lemon, peach, grape
2   If you feel 'blue' are you feeling (cold, happy, sad)?
3   Which continent contains China, Japan and India?
4   How many legs has a gnat?
    three, six, eight
5   Blood travels from the heart to other parts of the body in
    (arteries, tendons, hoses).
6   Whyalla, Port Pirie and Renmark are towns in (South Australia,
    Queensland, Western Australia).
7   If you are taking 'forty winks' you are (playing, hoping, sleeping).
8   How many stars are there on the Australian flag?
    three, six, five
9   Horse is to neigh as elephant is to (moo, screech, trumpet).
10 A song for two people is called a (duet, solo, trio).

General Knowledge

1. Which animal appears on the Australian five-cent coin?
2. Name two mammals which lay eggs.
3. What creature is known as Australia's native dog?
4. In what sport do you use a shuttlecock, net and racquet?
5. What are chihuahuas and retrievers?
6. What two planets begin with 'M'?
7. The letters of this man's name help tell us the colours of the rainbow — Roy G Biv. Write down the name of each colour.
8. Would a motorist be walking or driving?
9. In what part of your body would you find a bridge?
10. Which of these is the odd one out?
    hurricane, cyclone, tornado, torpedo

General Knowledge

1. Which of these is a mammal?
   dog, alligator, spider, canary
2. For what was Henry Lawson famous?
3. What is a lasso?
4. Write these words in alphabetical order:
   chest, chain, chubby, chicken, chocolate
5. For what do the letters NZ stand?
6. What is strange about the word 'bookkeeper'?
7. What types of creatures are funnel-webs, widows and red-backs?
8. In what sport are clubs, balls and tees used?
9. Rearrange all the letters of 'pier' to get something ready to eat.
10. What does an optician do?

General Knowledge

1 Rearrange the letters of 'bruise' to get precious stones.
2 Use one word to replace the underlined words in this sentence.
   I will see you when I <u>come</u> <u>back</u> <u>again</u>.
3 What country is Wellington the capital of?
4 Which of these is a fungus plant?
   grass, toadstool, carnation
5 For what do the initials RSPCA stand?
6 Which is the odd one out?
   puppy, calf, cub, lion
7 What is lavender?
8 Name two animals covered with spines.
9 An instrument which attracts metals is called a __ __ __ __ __ __.
10 Write 21 in Roman numerals.

General Knowledge

1 What word is the opposite of 'maximum'?
2 What types of creatures are rosellas and curlews?
3 What continent contains the United States of America, Mexico and Canada?
4 How many sides has a quadrilateral?
5 In what Australian state would you find the Barossa Valley?
6 In what part of your body would you find your cranium?
7 From what fruit is most wine made?
8 Which two animals appear on Australia's coat of arms?
9 Name two musical instruments with strings.
10 What is the name given to a room below ground level?

General Knowledge

1. What is the name given to a room at the top of a house?
2. For what do the initials COD stand?
3. What instrument does a doctor use to listen to your heartbeat?
4. What five-letter word means the opposite of full?
5. Give a word that means the opposite of ancient.
6. What type of creature is a kelpie?
7. What is this number — XXIV?
8. Which biblical character was said to have been swallowed by a whale?
9. What months of the year are our summer season?
10. Which word is out of place?
    guitar, daffodil, pansy, violet

General Knowledge

1. Nose is to smell as hand is to __ __ __ __ __ .
2. In which Australian state is the city of Broken Hill?
3. How many planets are there in our solar system?
4. Who was able to wear the glass slipper on her foot?
5. What is the name given to a place where money is made?
6. If you mix red and yellow paint, what colour do you make?
7. Which is the odd one out?
    onion, banana, orange, plum
8. Rearrange all the letters of 'listen' to get a Christmas decoration.
9. Name our five senses.
10. What is a mixture of smoke and fog called?

General Knowledge

1   Americans call it 'gasoline'. What do we call it?
2   What sort of plant did Jack climb in the nursery tale?
3   What type of creatures are gnats and lice?
4   What do the initials RSVP mean?
5   Which is the odd one out?
    ankle, foot, knee, toe, elbow
6   What five-letter word means the opposite of birth?
7   Which Australian state features a black swan on its flag?
8   What does 'bite the dust' mean?
9   What sport are greens, tees and fairways associated with?
10 Which animal is featured on the reverse side of a twenty-cent piece?

General Knowledge

1   In what country is Disneyland?
2   What is Big Ben?
3   Write down the silent letters in each of these words:
    lamb, knight, thistle
4   In what country would you find the Eiffel Tower?
5   What is the name given to a huge distance run in athletics?
6   What does 'hold your tongue' mean?
7   Complete this saying: 'Don't count your _ _ _ _ _ _ _ _
    before they are hatched'.
8   In which nursery rhyme did the mouse run up the clock?
9   How many playing cards are there in an ordinary pack?
10 For what sport is a velodrome used?

Spot the changes

Look carefully at the two pictures. In the second picture at least ten changes have been made. Can you spot them all? Write your answers on a sheet of paper.

Betty and things that start with 'B'

How many things starting with the letter 'B' can you find in this picture of Betty with the burglar?

Puzzles

Spot the errors

Our artist deliberately made mistakes in these pictures to try to trick you. Can you work out what is wrong in each picture?

Dotty colour

Colour all the shapes with dots in them and you will discover a beautiful scene.

Matching pairs

A lot of socks were washed this week, but when they were brought in dry, they became jumbled. Can you sort them into pairs? Draw lines to join the pairs.

Line puzzles

Can you draw the two figures below in one continuous line, without crossing a line, tracing a line, or lifting your pencil from the paper?

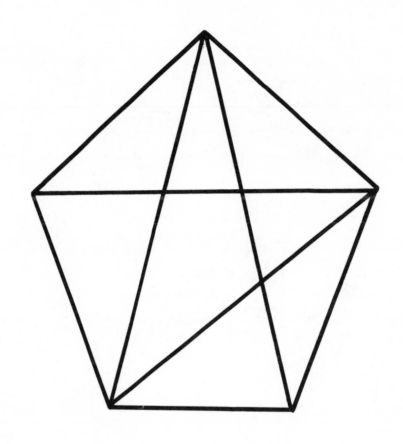

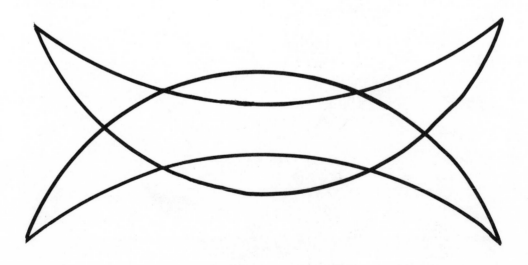

Hidden objects

Our artist has hidden some toys in this picture. How many can you find?

Amazing maze

Help the poor bird find its nest.

What's missing?

Complete the missing part of the drawing.

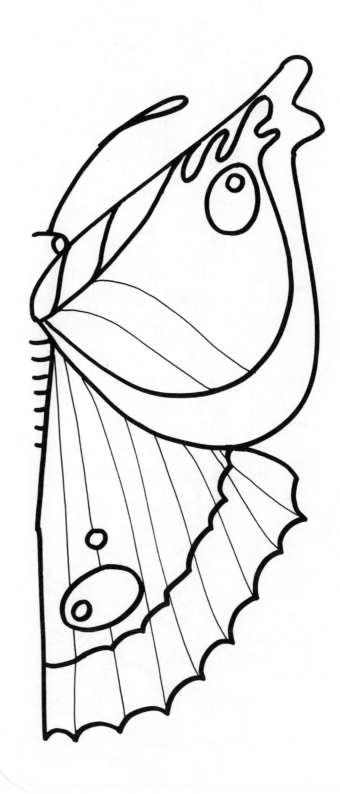

Jumbled pictures

Here are six pictures that have been jumbled up. Write down the correct order for the pictures.

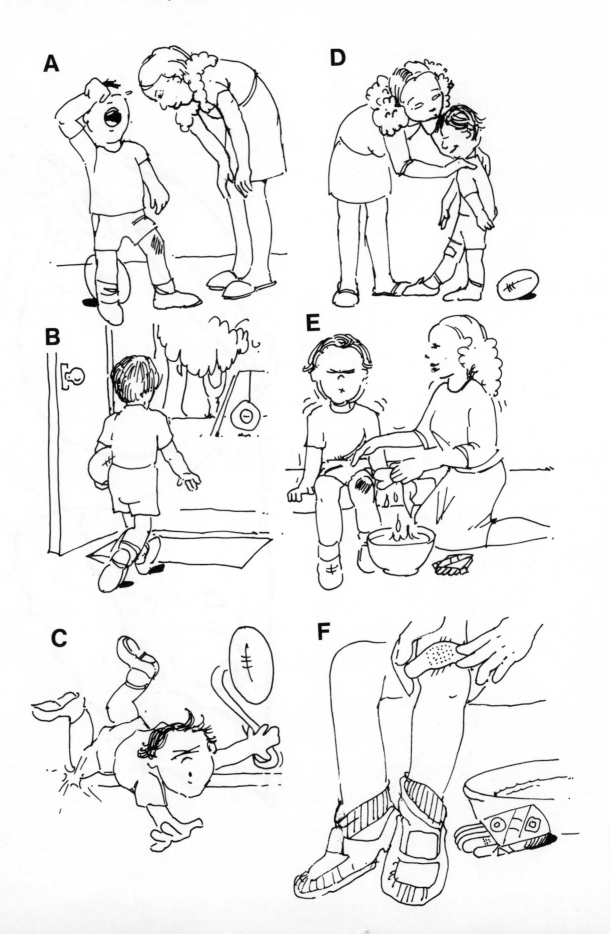

Who won?

Mary, John and Susan had a bicycle race. Only one finished. Who was it?

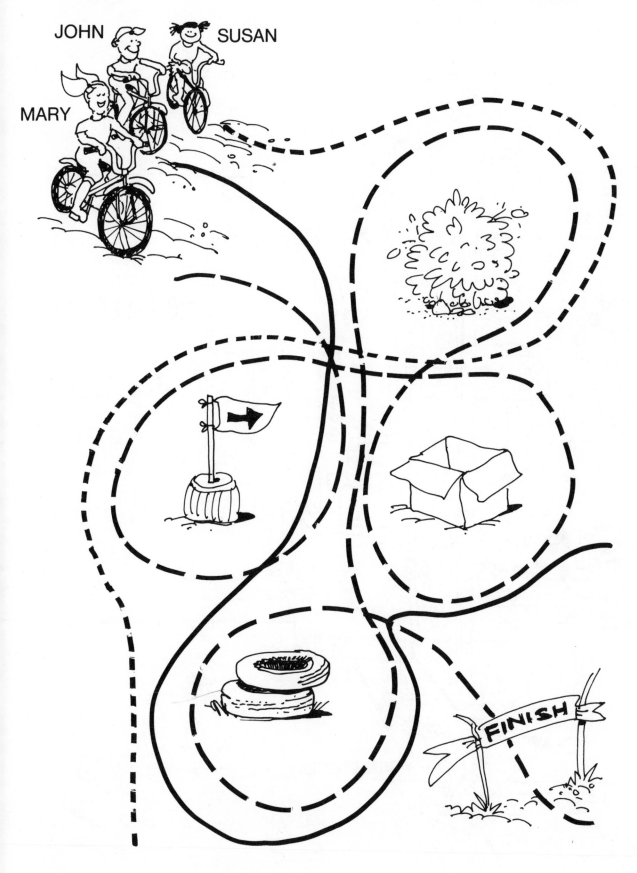

Corey and things that start with 'C'

How many things starting with the letter 'C' can you find in this picture of Corey near the cupboard?

Spot the changes

Look carefully at the two pictures. In the second picture at least 15 changes have been made. Can you spot them all? Write your answers on a sheet of paper.

Spot the errors

When our artist drew this picture he wasn't feeling very well and he made some mistakes. Can you find at least 15 mistakes he has made?

Who's lost?

The Smith family have come from Sydney and they want to go to Melbourne. Someone has turned the signpost around and they don't know which road to take. Can you help them?

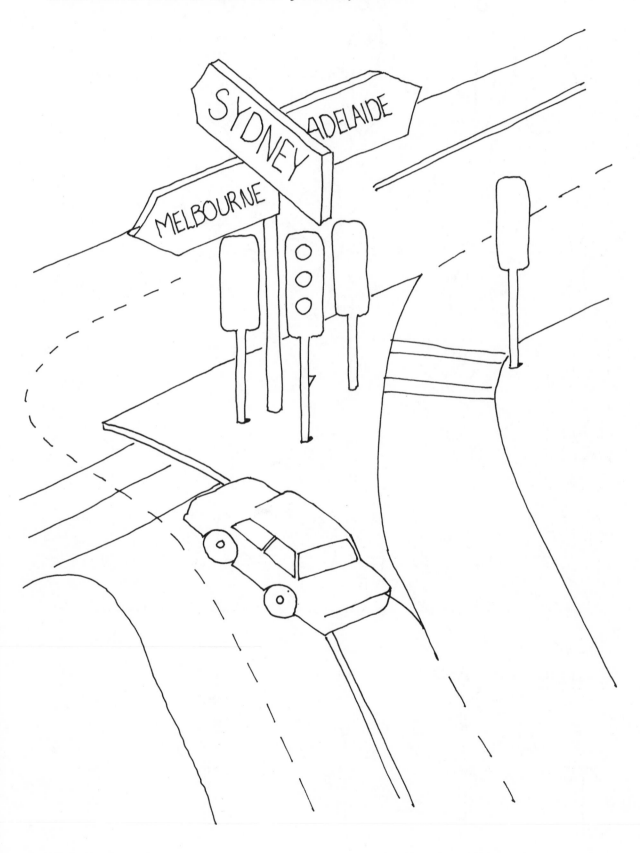

Puzzles

ACTIVITY **16**

Look-alikes

Find the two figures in each row that are exactly alike.

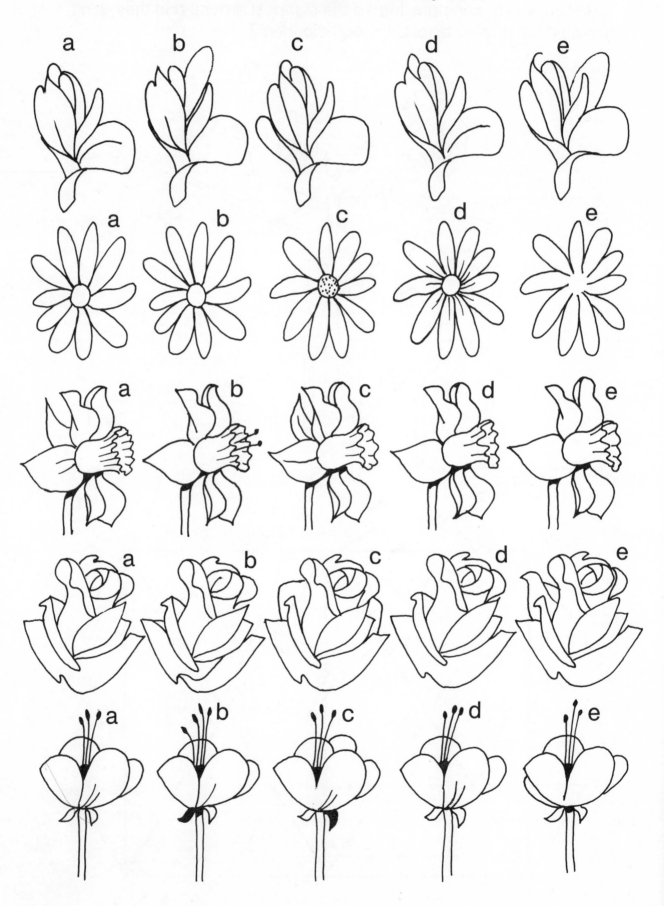

Look-alikes

Line puzzles

Can you draw the two figures below in one continuous line without crossing a line, tracing a line, or lifting your pencil from the paper?

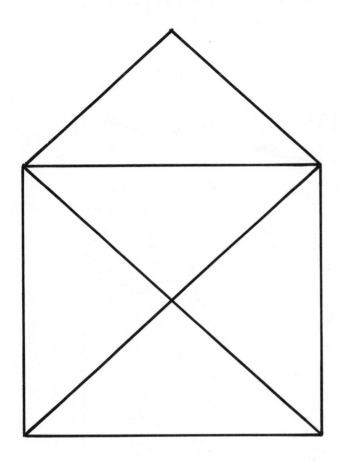

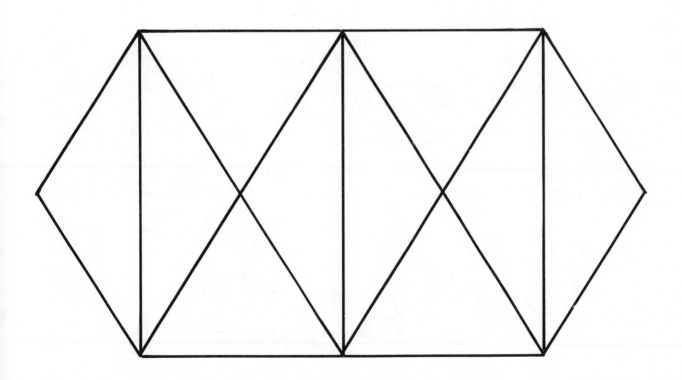

Memory test

Below are twenty common objects. Study them carefully for one minute, then cover the picture and see if you can remember them all by writing down the names of each one on a sheet of paper.

Amazing maze

Find a path through the maze
to help the plane find the airport.

What's missing?

Complete the missing part of the drawing.

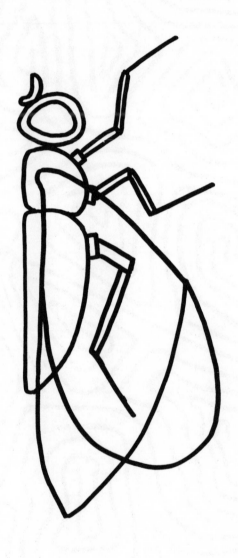

Spinning top

You will need:
a piece of cardboard (an empty cereal packet will do)
a pencil
coloured paints or pencils

What to do:
With your compass, trace out a circle on the cardboard.
Find the exact centre (the hole made by the compass point) and make the hole just big enough to take the pencil.
Mark the cardboard into segments and paint each segment a different colour, or do a spiral design, starting from the centre.
Push the pencil into the centre.
Spin the top between your fingers and let go.

A windmill

You will need:
some light cardboard
an ice-block stick
a drawing pin
a ruler
a pencil
paints
scissors

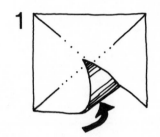

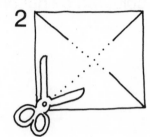

What to do:
Cut a 150 mm square from the light card.
Draw lines from corner to corner and colour the four triangles in different colours.
Cut from each corner, half way to the centre.
Fold the right hand corner of each triangle to the centre and push the pin through to hold them in place.
Pin your windmill to the top of the stick so that the windmill will spin in the wind.

Pop-up spider

You will need:
a piece of stiff paper 30 cm x 10 cm
a piece of thin cardboard 20 cm x 15 cm

Card

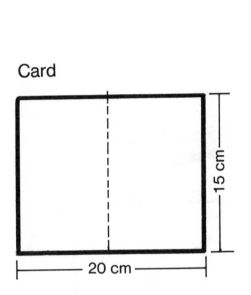

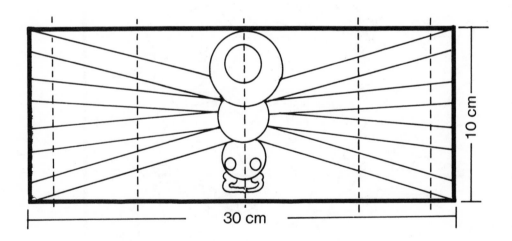

What to do:
Draw the spider on the paper.
Fold him, up and down, along the dotted lines.
Fold the cardboard in half.
Glue the spider's feet onto each side.
When the glue is dry, fold the card in half with the spider inside.
When the card is opened the spider will pop up.

Crinkle art

Take a piece of art paper and screw it up. Now straighten out the paper and by using crayons or coloured pencils, trace over some of the creases and crinkles to make an attractive pattern.

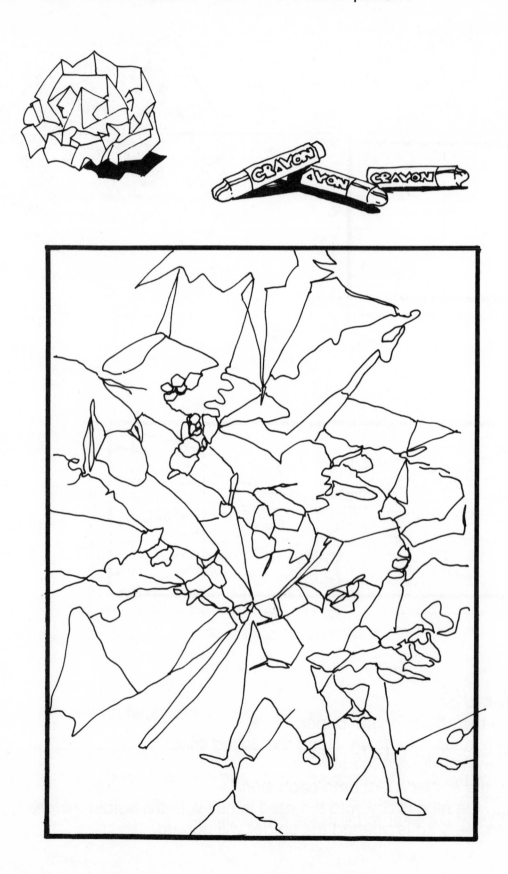

The fish in the bowl

You will need:
a piece of stiff cardboard 3 cm x 3 cm

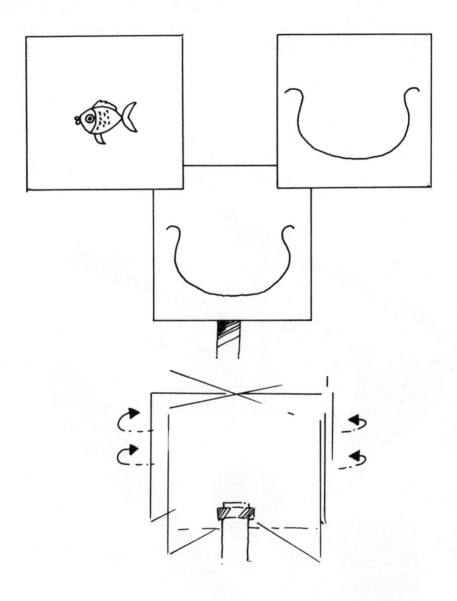

What to do:
Draw a fish on one side of the cardboard and a bowl on the other side.
Tape the cardboard to a pencil.
Hold the pencil between your hands and rub your hands back and forth to spin the pencil.
The fish will appear to be in the bowl.

Pictures without a camera

Paint all over the surface of a large sheet of paper. Choose a bright blue or red colour. When it has dried, place the paper in the hot sun and on top of it, place a number of objects with interesting shapes. Leave them in the sun for a few hours. When you return, you will find that the sun has faded the exposed areas of paint, leaving you a shape picture of all the objects.

Super soap boat

This boat can push itself through the water.

You will need:
a piece of aluminium foil 15 cm x 15 cm
a piece of soap 2 cm x 3 cm

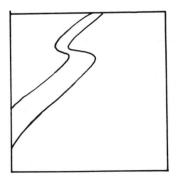

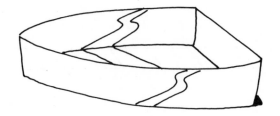

What to do:
Make the aluminium foil into the shape of a boat.
Carve a hook 'engine' from the soap (see diagram).
Place the 'engine' on the rear of your boat.
When you place your boat in a dish of water, it will race across the surface of the water.

Super straw plane

A straw plane is easy to make and lots of fun to fly.

You will need:
a drinking straw
a sheet of thick paper or thin cardboard

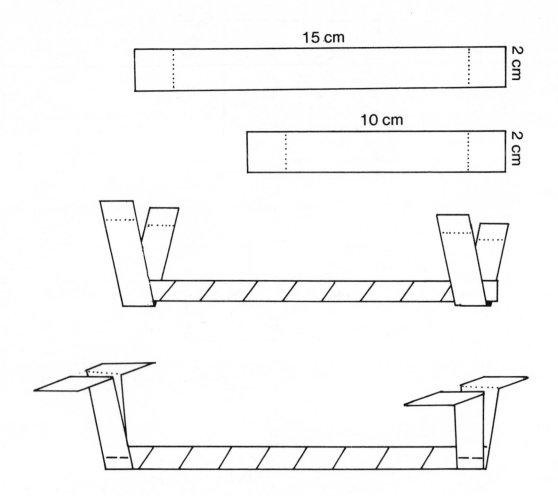

What to do:
Cut out the rear wing section from the paper (15 cm x 2 cm).
Cut out the front wing section from the paper (10 cm x 2 cm).
Fold both wings in half.
Flatten the straw and place one end inside the folded front wing and staple together, and the other end inside the folded back wing and staple together. Staple the wings together just below the dotted lines (see diagram)
Fold the wing tips outwards, along the dotted line.
Now your plane is ready to fly.

A colour wheel

Cut a circle out of light, stiff cardboard, 6 cm to 8 cm in diameter.
Divide the circle into three equal parts. Colour one part of the circle
blue, one red, and one yellow. Punch two holes through the circle of
card near the centre. Now loop two pieces of string, 60 cm long,
through the holes and tie the ends together.
Hold the ends of the loops in each hand and while the wheel hangs
loosely, swing it round and round in circles a dozen or more times.
Pull on the loops to start the wheel spinning. Watch the colours of the
wheel closely.

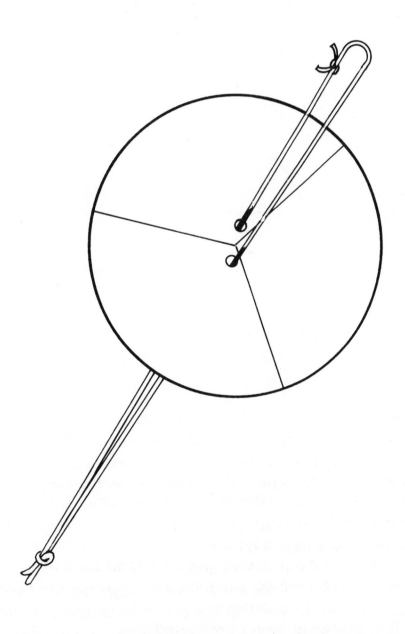

The two boxers

You will need:
cardboard
elastic

Front   Back   Elastic

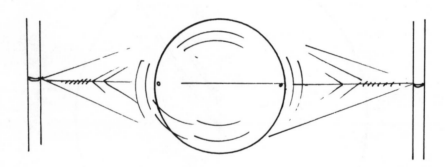

What to do:
Cut a 5 cm diameter circle out of the cardboard.
Make two holes in the cardboard at opposite sides of the circle.
Draw the figure of a boxer on one side of the card near one of the
holes and facing in to the centre of the card. Then draw the figure of a
boxer on the opposite side of the card, near the other hole, also facing
the centre of the card (see diagram). Be sure to get the positions right,
otherwise the result will look a bit silly.
Thread elastic through the holes as shown and tie each end to some
kind of support, stretch until the elastic is just beginning to stretch.
Then 'wind up' the card by twisting the elastic over and over. When it
is wound up enough, let go and watch the figures on the card. They
will look as if they are boxing each other.

Super noughts and crosses

I'm sure you can play noughts and crosses. However, this is 'Super' noughts and crosses. It is the same as the game you play — except that you try to get five noughts or five crosses in a row.

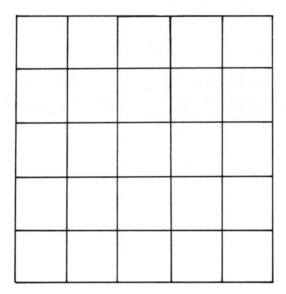

Who's last?

Try not to end up in prison — which is the last square. Two players take turns claiming 1, 2 or 3 squares at a time. Think carefully. Make sure it is your opponent and not you who is forced to occupy the last space. Write your initials in each space you claim.

20 Question game

One person thinks of something and others have to ask questions to guess what it is. Only twenty questions are allowed. Each answer is only 'yes' or 'no', eg
1   Is it an animal or from an animal?
2   Is it a plant or from a plant?
3   Is it a mineral?
4   Is it found in cities and towns?

The first person to guess the answer then thinks of something. If not guessed in twenty questions the same person goes again.

Listening

Listen with your eyes closed for twenty seconds, then write down all the sounds you heard.

Dazzling dominoes

For this game you will need some dominoes. Place all the dominoes face down and take turns with your partner to pick up a domino. If you pick up, say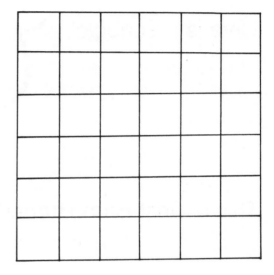

put a cross in the second row down, fourth row across, and so on.
The lowest number is always the 'down' row. Try to get three crosses in a row. If you happen to pick up a domino with a blank you must miss a turn.

Dice cricket

For this game you will need a normal dice. One player rolls the dice. If he throws a six, this is a 'wicket' — all other numbers are runs scored, ie 1, 2, 3, 4 or 5. The player with the dice, 'the bowler', keeps rolling while the 'batsman' adds his score. When ten wickets, ie ten sixes have been thrown, that is the end of the innings, and the players swap after totalling the first batsman's score.

Scribbles

You can play a 'scribbles' game with two players, two pencils and some paper. The first player draws a 'scribble' on a piece of paper and the other tries to make the scribble into a picture. If the player makes a picture, they score a point. If they can't make a picture they do not score. Take it in turns to draw a scribble. Have ten tries each.

Here is a 'scribble'.

This is what Bruno turned it into.

Step words

This is a game for two or more players. The first player writes a word on a sheet of paper (across the page). His opponent must then write a word that begins with the last letter of that word. Both players take it in turns making words, for a given time, say three minutes. Score by giving 1 point for two- and three-letter words, 2 points for four-letter words, 3 points for five-letter words, and 4 points for six-, seven- and eight-letter words or more.

eg **e l e p h a n t**
r
y
i
n
g i r a f f e

Odds and evens

This game is best played in pairs. Both players have ten beads (or small stones). One player, hiding his hands behind his back, puts a number of beads into one hand and presents this closed hand to his opponent, at the same time announcing whether his closed hand contains an odd or even number. The other player must try to guess the exact number. If he guesses correctly, he takes all the beads in the hand. If he fails to guess correctly, he must give the other player the difference between his guess and the actual number.

If the player had three beads in his closed hand, and the guess was five, the player who guesses must give the other player two beads.

Players take turns until one player has all the beads.

How many?

The idea of this game is to be the first to come up with the longest list. It can be played in pairs or groups. All each player needs is a pencil and some paper.

One player chooses a subject, eg birds, animals, fruits, vegetables, cars, boys' names, girls' names or flowers.

Now, in three minutes, all players work and think frantically to see who can write down the longest list. When time is up the person with the most written down is the winner.

eg Birds — eagle, wren, sparrow, hawk, dove and so on.

Instead of subjects, you may choose words beginning with a particular letter of the alphabet.

Answers

Word puzzles

Find the 'sh'
Ship, shore, bush, fish, shovel, shirt, shell, shade, cash, leash, rash, sash, shark, shoe, shop, etc.

Word wheel
Eat, eaten, at, ate, ten, tent, tenth, the, there, here, her, reel(s), eel(s), spin, pin, in, pine, spine, neat, etc.

Scrambled soup
Bacon, onions, corn, meat, tomatoes, salt, carrots, potatoes.

How well do you read?
Self-correcting

Scrambled words
1 saw, was; 2 war, raw; 3 rat, tar; 4 but, tub; 5 eat, ate; 6 name, mane; 7 late, tale; 8 meat, mate; 9 tame, team.

Find the word
Easter

Creature crossword
Across: 1 fish, 3 bear, 4 seal, 6 monkey
Down: 2 horse, 3 bee, 5 lion

Word grid
Bread, bacon, rice, eggs, apple, cheese, meat, cream, flour, carrots, jam, pickles.

Activity 9

Anagrams
1 ten, 2 raw, 3 ring, 4 ship, 5 west, 6 post, 7 owl, 8 star, 9 finger, 10 plum.

Activity 10

Word pieces
1 milk, stop; 2 ball, coat; 3 nine, wind; 4 duck, shut; 5 farm, from; 6 bird, meat; 7 soft, door; 8 baby, swim.

Activity 11

Keep a secret
Wipe your feet before entering our home.

Activity 12

Words from words
Self-correcting

Activity 13

What's the word?
1 gate, 2 baby, 3 nest, 4 milk, 5 rain, 6 moon, 7 roof, 8 gold, 9 bone, 10 cake.

Activity 14

Join-up
Starfish, cowboy, buttercup, lighthouse, armchair, tablecloth.

Activity 15

The same letters
1 seat, east; 2 shore, horse; 3 mate, tame; 4 finger, fringe; 5 listen, silent; 6 charm, march; 7 cedar, cared; 8 battle, tablet; 9 table, bleat; 10 statue, astute.

Activity 16

Hard to easy
Hard, card, cart, cast, east, easy.

Activity 17

What's the opposite?
1 light, 2 night, 3 old, 4 cold, 5 rough, 6 tough, 7 long, 8 strong, 9 tame, 10 same.

Activity 18

Hidden words

1 a, large, strange, ran, an, rang, get, the, there, her, here, ere, rein, in, of, oft, ten, tend, end, sire, red, etc.
2 to, get, her, the, there, ere, here, rear, ear, earl, a, all, low, sad, a, van, an, stow, tow, ward, war, art, is, deal, idea, etc.

Activity 19

Word-make
Answers will vary.

Activity 20

Missing letters
1 balloon, 2 cheese, 3 rudder, 4 rabbit, 5 bottle, 6 jelly, 7 funnel, 8 poppy, 9 carrot, 10 dress.

Activity 21

Letter change
1 rope, 2 hand, 3 fight, 4 card, 5 water, 6 snow, 7 donkey, 8 barrow, 9 toast, 10 giant.

Activity 22

'Ssh!' silent letters
lamb, castle, knot, cupboard, thumb, thistle, ghost, sign, iron, yacht.

Activity 23

Animal Pieces
Crocodile, cockatoo, elephant, monkey, giraffe, panther, leopard, antelope, tiger, goat.

Activity 24

Wise old saying
Too many cooks spoil the broth.

Activity 25

How well do you read?
Self-correcting.

Activity 26

Scrambled words
1 dear, read; 2 meal, male; 3 steak, stake; 4 pool, loop; 5 pots, stop, post, tops; 6 lemon, melon; 7 steal, least, stale; 8 heart, earth.

Activity 27

Word grid

Pear, peace, aloud, cell, scent, steal, sun, inn, hare, hear, deer, blew, won.

Activity 28

Anagrams

1 march, 2 peach, 3 table, 4 bowl, 5 wasp, 6 north, 7 palm, 8 silent.

Activity 29

Word pieces

1 football, 2 tennis, 3 hockey, 4 athletics, 5 soccer, 6 golf, 7 chess, 8 boxing, 9 swimming, 10 cricket.

Activity 30

Keep a secret

Blue, green, gold, yellow, black, brown, purple, white.

Activity 31

Words from words

Answers will vary.

Activity 32

What's the word?

1 rabbit, 2 bucket, 3 kitten, 4 summer, 5 monkey, 6 needle, 7 button, 8 banana, 9 cheese, 10 church.

Activity 33

Where do they belong?

Food: hamburger, cannelloni, casserole, parsnip.
Clothing: shirt, blouse, leotard, tie.
Colours: aquamarine, ruby, purple, khaki.
Homes: apartment, stable, web, igloo.

Activity 34

Back-to-front words

1 school, 2 apple, 3 donkey, 4 dragon, 5 chocolate, 6 window, 7 elephant, 8 planet, 9 kitchen, 10 cupboard.

Activity 35

Slow to fast

Slow, blow, blot, boot, boat, coat, cost, cast, fast.

Jumbled animals

1 hare, 2 tiger, 3 bear, 4 lion, 5 mouse, 6 horse, 7 zebra, 8 panther, 9 goat, 10 donkey.

Activity 37

Find the fruits and vegetables

1 radish, 2 pear, 3 carrot, 4 cherry, 5 peach, 6 plum, 7 bean, 8 mango, 9 onion, 10 potato.

Activity 38

Word-make

Answers will vary.

Activity 39

What's the saying?

When the cat's away the mice will play.

Activity 40

Two in one

1 moon, star; 2 orange, lemon; 3 lounge, table; 4 zebra, tiger; 5 white, blue; 6 blouse, shirt; 7 bacon, mutton; 8 hockey, soccer.

Maths puzzles

Activity 1

Planet Puzzler

Uranus

Activity 2

Find the squares

There are 14 squares.

Activity 3

Maths cross

1	4	4	▨
2	▨	2	1
1	6	▨	2
▨	4	0	0

Activity 4

Number codes
1 camel, 2 bear, 3 lion.

Activity 5

Magic triangle

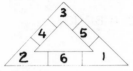

Activity 6

Magic squares

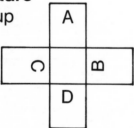

Activity 7

Maths puzzles
1 27, all the other numbers are even
2 C
3 12

Activity 8

Circle patterns
Self-correcting.

Activity 9

Four square
Move A up

```
        ┌───┐
        │ A │
    ┌───┼───┼───┐
    │ C │   │ B │
    └───┼───┼───┘
        │ D │
        └───┘
```

Activity 10

Crack the code
1 bus, 2 van, 3 lorry

Activity 11

Where do they fit?

2	1
3	4

Activity 12

Funny fifteens

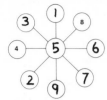

Activity 13

Tricky twelves

Activity 14

Number cross

Activity 15

Number codes

1 owl, 2 wren, 3 hawk

Activity 16

Dot-to-dot

Self-correcting.

Activity 17

Magic squares

9			12			18		
5	2	2	3	3	6	11	2	5
0	3	6	7	4	1	0	6	12
4	4	1	2	5	5	7	10	1

Activity 18

Maths puzzles

1 4, 2 only once. After you take 3 from 18 it becomes 15, 3 they all have,
4 22, 5 11 — the others can all be divided equally by three.

Activity 19

Colour by numbers
Self-correcting.

Activity 20

Number maze

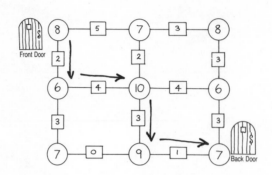

General Knowledge

Activity 1

1 4, 2 General Post Office, 3 javelin throwing, 4 a type of bat, 5 the eye,
6 Little Red Riding Hood, 7 June, 8 a bear, 9 not well, 10 Los Angeles.

Activity 2

1 a type of white wine, 2 the ear, 3 eight, 4 tennis, 5 bomb, cannon, gun, rifle,
6 a small waterhole, 7 curtain, 8 winter, 9 radish, 10 exit.

Activity 3

1 please turn over, 2 Victoria, 3 ruler, 4 get into trouble, 5 throat, 6 Mister,
photograph, avenue, 7 bunch, 8 Jack and Jill, 9 skunk, 10 Alice in
Wonderland.

Activity 4

1 Venus, 2 dogs, 3 red, amber, green, 4 purple, 5 horse racing, 6 a doctor
who performs operations, 7 white, 8 spider, 9 plum, 10 100.

Activity 5

1 cat, 2 musical instruments, 3 eagle, hawk, vulture, etc, 4 archery, darts or
rifle shooting, 5 a spider, 6 red, white and blue, 7 to give away a secret, 8
steward or stewardess, or hostess, 9 January, March, May, July, August,
October and December, 10 25th April.

Activity 6

1 wallet, 2 chess, 3 pig, 4 flowers, 5 a e i o u, 6 skeleton, 7 station, 8 red, 9
mate, 10 head.

Activity 7

1 trumpet, bugle, cornet, saxaphone, recorder, etc, 2 alligator, 3 meat, 4 camera, 5 leopard, 6 Holland, 7 March, 8 New South Wales, 9 they all read the same backwards or forwards, 10 three.

Activity 8

1 acorn, 2 Humpty Dumpty, 3 tennis, 4 mare, 5 X-rays, 6 broth, 7 take, 8 beaver, 9 Sydney, 10 heart.

Activity 9

1 bushranger, 2 bee, 3 Canberra, 4 frog, 5 three, 6 ape, giraffe, lion, monkey, 7 ear, 8 eagle, 9 kennel, 10 being silly.

Activity 10

1 stable, 2 giraffe, 3 Victoria, 4 wise, smart, sensible, etc, 5 petal, 6 boxing, 7 ring, 8 vase, 9 cutlery, 10 sheep.

Activity 11

1 six, 2 surfing, 3 p, 4 ostrich, penguin, emu, cassowary, kiwi, etc, 5 Victoria, 6 milk, 7 China, 8 herd, 9 fish, 10 mouth.

Activity 12

1 lemon, 2 sad, 3 Asia, 4 six, 5 arteries, 6 South Australia, 7 sleeping, 8 six, 9 trumpet, 10 duet.

Activity 13

1 echidna, 2 platypus and echidna, 3 dingo, 4 badminton, 5 dogs, 6 Mercury, Mars, 7 red, orange, yellow, green, blue, indigo, violet, 8 driving, 9 nose, 10 torpedo.

Activity 14

1 dog, 2 he was a poet and story writer, 3 a rope with a noose, used by cowboys. 4 chain, chest, chicken, chocolate, chubby, 5 New Zealand, 6 it has three sets of consecutive double letters. 7 spiders, 8 golf, 9 ripe, 10 cares for eyes.

Activity 15

1 rubies, 2 return, 3 New Zealand, 4 toadstool, 5 Royal Society for the Prevention of Cruelty to Animals, 6 lion, 7 a plant, 8 anteater, echidna, hedgehog, 9 magnet, 10 XXI.

Activity 16

1 minimum, 2 birds, 3 North America, 4 four, 5 South Australia, 6 head,
7 grapes, 8 kangaroo and emu, 9 guitar, violin, viola, cello, bass.
10 basement, cellar.

Activity 17

1 attic, 2 cash on delivery, 3 stethoscope, 4 empty, 5 modern, 6 dog, 7 24,
8 Jonah, 9 December, January, February, 10 guitar.

Activity 18

1 touch, 2 New South Wales, 3 nine, 4 Cinderella, 5 mint, 6 orange, 7 onion,
8 tinsel, 9 taste, hearing, sight, touch, smell, 10 smog.

Activity 19

1 petrol, 2 beanstalk, 3 insects, 4 reply soon please, 5 elbow, 6 death,
7 Western Australia, 8 fall over, 9 golf, 10 platypus.

Activity 20

1 United States of America, 2 a famous clock in London, 3 b, k, t, 4 France,
5 marathon, 6 stop talking, be quiet, 7 chickens, 8 Hickory Dickory Dock,
9 52, 10 cycling.

Puzzles

Activity 1

Spot the changes
Self-correcting

Activity 2

Betty and things that start with 'b'
Self-correcting

Activity 3

Spot the errors
Elephant's tail, spider only has 6 legs, a three dollar note, car with square
tyres, train wheels, bird's beak.

Activity 4

Dotty colour
Self-correcting.

Activity 5

Matching pairs
Self-correcting

Activity 6

Line puzzles
1 Starting at A, draw a line through points B, C, D, E, C, A, D and B.

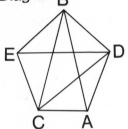

Diag 1.

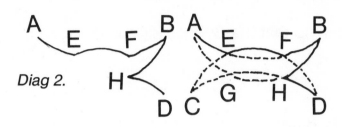

Diag 2.

2 Starting at B, draw a line through points A, E, F, B, H, D, F, E, C, H, A

Activity 7

Hidden objects
Self-correcting

Activity 8

Amazing maze
Self-correcting.

Activity 9

What's missing
Self-correcting.

Activity 10

Jumbled pictures
B C A E F D

Activity 11

Who won?
Mary

Activity 12

Corey and things that start with 'c'
Self-correcting

Activity 13

Spot the changes
Self-correcting

Activity 14

Spot the errors
Self-correcting

Activity 15

Who's lost?
Turn the signpost so that the Sydney sign is pointing the way they have come.

Activity 16

Look-alikes
a and d, a and b, d and e, a and d, a and d.

Activity 17

Line puzzles

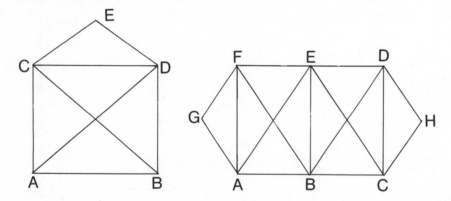

1 Starting at A, draw a line through points B, C, D, E, C, A, D and B.

2 Starting at B, draw a line through points A, E, B, D, H, C, D, E, C, B, F, G, A, F, E.

Activity 18

Memory test
Self-correcting.

Activity 19

Amazing maze
Self-correcting.

Activity 20

What's missing?
Self-correcting.

Classroom TIMESAVERS

CLASSROOM TIMESAVERS UNLIMITED and
MORE CLASSROOM TIMESAVERS UNLIMITED
bring you just that.

Each book contains over 180 pages of *fully reproducible* forms, diagrams, awards and certificates plus hundreds of simple illustrations covering dozens of themes.

GEOGRAPHY TIMESAVERS is the first in the series to concentrate on a specific area of the curriculum. The dozens of map outlines, graphs and diagrams will prove a highly valuable aid to all teachers.

Join the thousands of Australian teachers who have already discovered TIMESAVERS – invaluable resources, saving hours of preparation time.

Ashton Scholastic